Usborne English R

Level 3

A Midsummer Night's Dream

Retold by Mairi Mackinnon

Illustrated by Simona Bursi

English language consultant: Peter Viney

You can listen to the story online here:
www.usborneenglishreaders.com/
midsummernightsdream

Contents

It's easy to confuse the characters in A Midsummer Night's Dream, especially these four. So, to help you, at the start of the play...

...Lysander and Hermia are in love,

but Demetrius also loves Hermia,

and Helena loves Demetrius.

What will happen next?

The words shown like this are taken directly from the play.

"Four days!" said Duke Theseus. "Four days until we're married. It seems such a long time!"

Hippolyta smiled. "The time will soon pass, I'm sure, and your people need to be ready for the wedding."

"You're right." Theseus turned to his servants. "Go out into the city. I want everyone in Athens to celebrate and be happy with us."

"But wait, who's this? Egeus?"

An angry man came into the hall, with two younger men and a girl. "Duke Theseus, I need your help. My daughter Hermia won't listen to me. I have chosen this man, Demetrius, to be her husband. Now *this* man, Lysander, has stolen her heart – singing her songs, giving her presents and telling her that he loves her. She won't do what I say. Theseus, you know our law. Hermia must obey me and marry Demetrius, or die."

Theseus looked at Hermia. "Child, you must respect your father. He gave you life. If he really wants to, he can end your life, too. Demetrius is a good man."

"So is Lysander!" said Hermia fiercely. "Why can't my father understand? Would he really kill me?"

"If not, you'll have to live in a convent and you'll never see any men again. Is that what you want, Hermia? Think about it, and give me your answer before my wedding."

Lysander stepped forward. "Duke Theseus, I'm as good as Demetrius in every way – but I truly love Hermia, and I don't believe he does. He used to love her friend, Helena, and Helena still adores him."

You have her father's love, Demetrius;
Let me have Hermia's.

"I had heard that," said Theseus. "Egeus and Demetrius, I need to talk to you. But Hermia, remember, you owe your father everything. You must obey him."

Theseus and the others left the hall, and Lysander and Hermia were alone.

"I hate to see you so unhappy," said Lysander. "You know, true love has never been easy. So often, when two people love each other, they are separated by families or friends, by war or death or sickness."

Hermia took his hands. "You're right, my darling. It's a test, and we must show that our love is strong enough."

"Not all places have the same laws as Athens, Hermia. I have an aunt in another city. She will look after us. Are you brave enough to run away from your father? If you are, let's meet in the forest tomorrow night."

"I'll be there!" said Hermia, smiling for the first time. "Look, here's poor Helena."

Helena was almost crying. "Oh, Hermia, I wish I could be more like you! The way you look, the way you speak… Then Demetrius would love me."

"I don't do anything to make him love me," said Hermia. "I frown at him, I'm angry with him, but he follows me everywhere."

"I smile at him and speak gently, but he just avoids me," said Helena.

"Don't worry," said Hermia. "Soon he won't see me, and he'll forget about me. Lysander and I are running away."

"We know we can trust you," said Lysander. "We're meeting in the forest tomorrow night, and then we're leaving Athens forever. Hermia, we should go. Helena, wish us luck. I hope that Demetrius will come back to you."

Helena watched them leave. "Everyone in Athens thinks I'm as pretty as she is," she said, "except for Demetrius. He used to say he loved me, but when he saw Hermia, he changed his mind. Now he doesn't even speak to me. Maybe he'll listen if I tell him what I know. He might even thank me. At least he might give me one kind word."

Is all our company here?

In another part of the city, six workmen were meeting to read a play.

"Are we all here?" asked Peter Quince.

"Read out all the names," said Nick Bottom. "No, first tell us what the play is."

"It's a comedy," said Quince, "about the tragic death of Pyramus and Thisbe. We'll perform it on the Duke's wedding night. Bottom, you'll be Pyramus, who kills himself for love."

"Oh," said Bottom. "I'll make that very tragic. People will cry and cry when they see me."

"Francis Flute?" Quince continued. "You'll be the lady Thisbe."

"I can't be a lady!" said Flute. "I'm growing a beard."

"Then let me be Thisbe," said Bottom. "I can speak in a sweet, high voice, like this."

"No, Bottom, you must be Pyramus." Quince gave out the other parts. "Snug, you're the lion."

"Please let me be the lion," said Bottom. "I can roar really loudly."

"Then you'll frighten all the ladies," said Quince, "and we'll be in trouble."

"All right, I'll roar very gently, like a mouse," said Bottom.

"Please, Bottom," said Quince. "You'll be perfect as Pyramus. Now, everyone, take your parts and learn them. We'll have a practice in the forest tomorrow night."

The forest was cool and quiet in the moonlight. Two fairies met in a clearing between the trees.

"I know you," said one. "You're one of the Fairy Queen's servants. I hope she's not coming here tonight."

"And I know you. You're Puck. You play tricks on people to make King Oberon laugh, don't you?"

"I do," said Puck proudly. "I make people fall over, and drop things, and lose their way at night – all kinds of fun. But listen, this is serious. Oberon is angry with Titania because she has a beautiful human boy, the son of an Indian princess. Titania adores him. Oberon wants the boy to be his servant, but Titania won't let him. Wait, here comes Oberon now."

"And here's Titania!" said the fairy. "This doesn't look good."

The Fairy King and Queen stared at each other coldly. "Let's go," Titania told her servants. "I have nothing to say to him."

"Wait," said Oberon. "I'm your husband. You should obey me in everything. All I want is a boy to serve me."

Give me that boy!

"You shall not have him," said Titania. "His mother was my dear friend, and she died when he was born. I promised to take good care of him. He's mine!" She turned and left, with her fairies following.

"She will regret this!" said Oberon. "Puck, listen to me. I know a magic flower. I'll tell you where to find it. When a person is sleeping, you put the flower juice on their eyes. Then when the person wakes up, they'll fall in love with the first living thing that they see. I'll use it to trick Titania."

"I'd like to see that!" said Puck. "I'll bring it to you right away."

Oberon was about to leave, too, when he heard human voices. Helena was following Demetrius into the clearing.

"Leave me alone!" said Demetrius. "I'm going to find Hermia, and kill Lysander. Go away. It makes me sick to look at you."

"It makes me sick when I *don't* look at you," said Helena.

"Huh! I don't love you and I never will."

"The more unkind you are, the more I love you. I'll never leave you," she said.

Demetrius walked on angrily, with Helena close behind.

"What a monster!" said Oberon. "Don't worry, sweet lady, before morning he will love you as much as he hates you now."

"Here I am, my lord," said Puck. He had the flower in his hand.

"Well done!" said Oberon. "Now, I'm going to find Titania, but I want you to keep some of the flower juice yourself. Look for a young man and a girl from Athens. You'll recognize their Athenian clothes. Put some juice on the young man's eyes, so that when he wakes up, he'll fall in love with the girl. Make sure she is the first thing that he sees. Then come back to me."

"I'll do that, sir," said Puck.

Lysander and Hermia wandered into the clearing. "My darling," said Lysander, "you should rest. We've come a long way and – and I think we might be lost. Look, you can lie down here, and I'll sleep over there." They were soon asleep.

"What's this?" Puck looked down at Lysander. "A man, in Athenian clothes! He's the one – and there's the poor girl, too. Well, he's sure to see her when he wakes up. I'll put the flower juice on his eyes, and go back to Oberon." He left without seeing Demetrius and Helena.

"Stop following me, you stupid girl!" Helena was exhausted, but Demetrius didn't care.

"I can't go any further. Please, stay with me," Helena begged him, but Demetrius had already gone. Then Helena looked down on the ground. "Lysander! Are you all right? Are you hurt?"

But who is here? Lysander! on the ground!

Lysander woke up. "Helena? Oh, most beautiful Helena, now I see you clearly. Where is that monster, Demetrius?"

"He's not a monster!" said Helena. "Even if he likes Hermia, I know Hermia loves you. I'm sure you'll be happy together."

"Happy with Hermia? No, what was I thinking? That was a kind of madness. You're the one that I love."

"You're laughing at me," said Helena. "It's bad enough that Demetrius doesn't love me, but now you're making fun of me too." She ran out of the clearing, crying.

"Wait!" Lysander ran after her. "Helena, I mean it!"

A few minutes later, Hermia woke up. "Lysander, help me! Save me from this horrible snake! No, it was only a dream – but Lysander, why don't you answer? Where have you gone?" She stood up and looked around. "Wherever you are, I'll find you, my love."

Bottom and the other workmen had found a place for their practice. "This can be our stage," said Bottom. "There's plenty of space. Now, I've looked at the play, and I think we should make a few changes."

"Why's that?" asked Quince.

"Well, we can't have Pyramus killing himself with a sword. The ladies won't like it at all. They'll be frightened of the lion, too. I have an idea, though. Before the play, we'll explain that it's all just pretending, and the lion isn't really a lion. Then everything will be all right. Now, let's start."

Puck watched them from behind a tree. "These are the worst actors I've ever seen! They don't know how funny they are. Ah, but I have an idea to make them funnier still."

Bottom left the clearing, and Puck said some magic words. Flute spoke, then Quince called, "Bottom! You need to come back in now... Bottom?" he shouted. "Bottom! Help!"

"What's wrong?" Bottom asked. "Why are you all running away?" He couldn't see what Puck had done. Now, instead of his own head, he had the head of a donkey.

"Oh, Bottom! You've changed!" said Flute.

"You're just trying to make me look stupid!" Bottom shouted after them. "I'm not frightened. I'm staying here." He started singing loudly: "EE-AW! EE-AW!"

"What's that lovely music?" said a sweet voice. "Please, don't stop." Titania had been asleep at the edge of the clearing. Now she sat up and looked adoringly at Bottom. "Oh, you beautiful man. Please, stay with me, and my fairy servants will make you comfortable. They'll bring you flowers and fruit and honey. They'll do anything you ask." Bottom looked surprised, but he sat down beside Titania. She put her arms around his thick neck, and kissed his long nose.

What angel wakes me from my flowery bed?

Puck laughed so much that he almost fell over. "This is because of the flower juice? It's even better than I imagined! I can't wait to tell Oberon!"

Oberon was delighted. "My clever Puck! And did you find the Athenian, too? Look, there he is."

Stand close: this is the same Athenian.

Demetrius was following Hermia into the clearing. "Um, no," said Puck. "That's the same girl, but it was a different man."

"What have you done to Lysander?" Hermia asked desperately. "If you've killed him, then please kill me too. I can't live without him."

"I haven't killed him," said Demetrius, "although I'd like to. I wouldn't do anything to make you unhappy, Hermia. Remember, I love you."

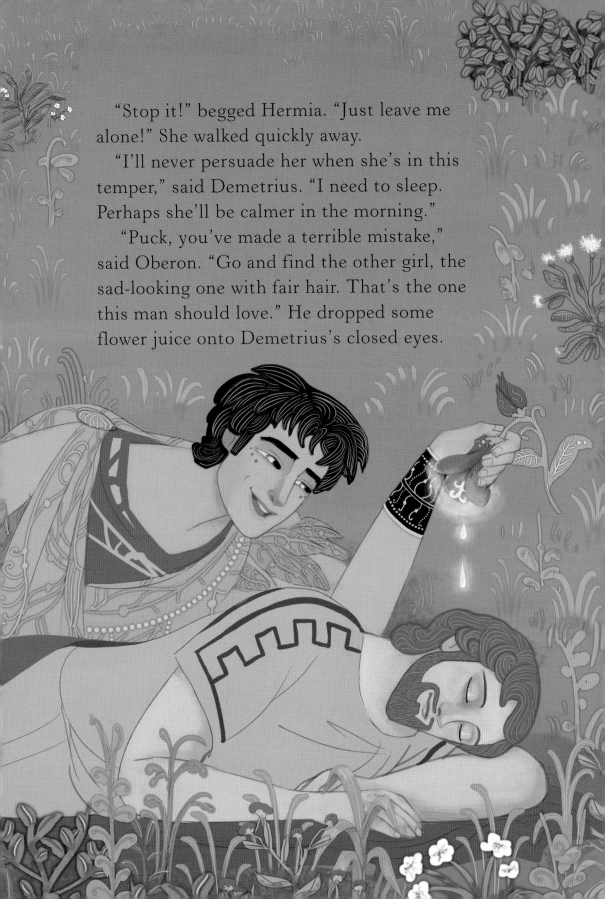

"Stop it!" begged Hermia. "Just leave me alone!" She walked quickly away.

"I'll never persuade her when she's in this temper," said Demetrius. "I need to sleep. Perhaps she'll be calmer in the morning."

"Puck, you've made a terrible mistake," said Oberon. "Go and find the other girl, the sad-looking one with fair hair. That's the one this man should love." He dropped some flower juice onto Demetrius's closed eyes.

Soon Helena and Lysander came into the clearing. "Please believe me," said Lysander. "I love you more than anything."

"You should tell Hermia that!" said Helena.

The sound of her voice woke Demetrius. "Helena, is that you? Oh, perfect beauty, let me kiss you."

"Demetrius, you can have Hermia if you want," said Lysander. "Let me be happy with Helena."

"Now you're both laughing at me," said Helena. "You're horrible!"

"Lysander, you know Hermia is your true love," said Demetrius. "Look, she's coming now."

Hermia ran towards them. "Oh Lysander, my sweet, why did you leave me?"

"Why should I stay?" asked Lysander. "I don't love you. In fact I hate you. You're ugly, an ugly little dark-haired thing."

"I don't understand," said Hermia. "What are you saying?"

She tried to put her arms around Lysander, and he shook her off. "Don't touch me!"

What love could press Lysander from my side?

Hermia turned angrily to Helena. "You've stolen my love from me in the night! How could you?"

Helena pushed her away. "And you're joining in their cruel trick. I thought you were my friend!"

"Don't worry, Helena, I won't let her hurt you," said Lysander.

"Won't you?" said Demetrius. "I'll protect Helena. I love her more than you do." He put his hand on his sword.

"Prove it!" said Lysander, taking his own sword.

"Please, help me!" Helena begged them. "She's always had a fierce temper, although she's only little."

What, have you come by night
And stolen my love's heart from him?

"Little?" screamed Hermia. "I'm tall enough to scratch your painted face and your empty eyes!"

"But I have longer legs to run away," answered the frightened Helena. Hermia ran after her, and Demetrius chased Lysander out of the clearing on the other side.

"Puck, this is all your fault," said Oberon. "We must make it right. Go after Lysander and Demetrius, and stop their fighting. Confuse them, and make them chase shadows until they are tired and sleep again. Then use the juice of this plant to take the spell off Lysander. When they all wake up, they'll think tonight was just a dream. I'll go to Titania and ask for her Indian boy, and then I'll take the spell off her too."

Lysander really was lost now. The night seemed much darker suddenly, and Demetrius kept moving from one place to another. "Demetrius, come out of there!" he shouted.

"I'm here, waiting for you," said Puck, in Demetrius's voice. "No, here!" he said from another direction. Then he raced through the trees to Demetrius. "Come out and show yourself!" he said in Lysander's voice. "You want to fight? I'm ready!"

Up and down, up and down,
I will lead them up and down.

"How can he do that?" wondered Lysander. "I run fast, but he is always faster. Well, I can't possibly find him in this darkness. I'll look for him tomorrow by daylight." He lay down and was soon asleep.

"I need to rest," said Demetrius.
"Tomorrow I'll find him more easily."
Without seeing Lysander, he lay down close by.

Helena wandered in. "I wish this night was over," she cried. "Tomorrow I'll go back to Athens. Maybe I can sleep for an hour or two first, and forget all this."

"Only three young people?" said Puck. "No, here's the fourth."

Hermia looked completely exhausted. "I can't go any further," she said. "I only hope Demetrius doesn't hurt Lysander. What a miserable night."

"Sleep, all of you," said Puck. He put the juice on Lysander's eyes. "Tomorrow you will recognize your true loves again, and all will be well."

Bottom was sitting on a bed of wild flowers. Titania was making a crown of flowers for his head, and stroking his ears. "What do you want, my love?" she asked. "What can I do for you?"

O, how I love thee!

"Tell your servants to scratch my head," said Bottom. "My face feels very hairy. Maybe I need a haircut. Oh, and I'm really hungry, too."

"Would you like some sweet honey?" asked Titania.

"I'd prefer hay," said Bottom. "There's nothing like good, fresh hay. Actually, I think I'll sleep a little first."

"Let me make you comfortable," said Titania, kissing Bottom's donkey face. She lay down beside him, and they both fell asleep.

Puck and Oberon were watching. "I'm beginning to feel sorry for her," said Oberon. "I saw her earlier, picking flowers for that monster. She loves it so much, it's embarrassing. I asked her for the Indian boy and she agreed without question. Let's take the spell off her now, and take the donkey head off that foolish man."

He put the juice on Titania's eyes. "Wake up, my sweet."

Now, my Titania; wake you, my sweet queen.

Titania sat up. "Oh, Oberon, it's the strangest thing. I thought I was in love with a donkey."

"You were, my love," smiled Oberon. "Look, there is your darling."

Titania screamed. "That thing? How horrible! How could I?"

There lies your love.

"It's all finished now," said Oberon. "Puck, take off his donkey head, and tomorrow he'll be himself again."

Fairy music played and the King and Queen smiled. They were friends at last.

"It's morning," said Puck. "I can hear hunting dogs. The Duke is coming."

"Let's go," said Titania to Oberon. "You can explain what happened later."

"It's a beautiful day," Theseus was saying to Hippolyta. "A fine morning for hunting… But who are these people, sleeping on the ground?"

Egeus stared at Hermia. "That's my daughter, sir!"

"Wasn't she going to tell us today whether she chooses Demetrius or the convent? Let's wake them."

My lord, this is my daughter here asleep.

Lysander and Demetrius, Hermia and Helena looked confused, then got up on their knees when they saw the Duke.

"Please, stand up," said Theseus. "Lysander and Demetrius, I thought you were enemies, but here you are sleeping side by side."

"My lord, I don't know what happened," said Lysander. "Hermia and I came here last night. We were planning to run away…"

"That's enough!" said Egeus. "Demetrius, do you hear? Theseus, you must punish them."

"Helena told me," Demetrius said to Theseus. "I followed them here, but – I don't know how it happened – all my love for Hermia has gone. It's Helena that I love now."

Theseus turned to Egeus. "Everyone is happy, it seems. I don't think we need to punish anyone. Let's have three weddings instead of one. Come, all of you, let's go back to the city."

In Athens, Quince and the other workmen were worried. "So nobody has seen Bottom since last night? What shall we do? We can't put on the play without him."

"Quince? Flute? Hurry up, boys, we must go to the palace," said Bottom's cheerful voice. "They've asked to see our play."

"Bottom, what happened to you? Thank goodness you're here!"

"I had such a strange dream," said Bottom. "I thought I was… I thought I had… I can't even tell you. You just wouldn't believe it."

I have had a dream.

Theseus, Hippolyta and the wedding guests finished their meal. "So now we're going to see a comedy, Egeus, is that right?"

"I've seen it already," said Egeus. "It's not very good, sir. They aren't real actors, just ordinary workmen."

"I'm sure they'll try hard," smiled Theseus.

Quince came on to the stage to explain the play. He read his part nervously, and introduced the other actors. "This is the hero, Pyramus, and the lovely lady Thisbe. This man is the wall that separated the two lovers. This man with his lantern is the moon, because the lovers met by moonlight, and this man is the lion."

"I hope the lion has a speaking part," said Theseus.

"The man in the moon ought to be inside his lantern," said Demetrius.

Bottom began to speak in a loud voice. He was enjoying himself. He tried to kiss Thisbe through a hole in the wall. "I kiss the wall, and not your lips at all," complained Thisbe. She agreed to meet Pyramus later, but she was frightened by a lion and dropped her long scarf. The lion picked up the scarf in his mouth and shook it.

Pyramus came back and found the scarf. He thought the lion had killed Thisbe, and made a long speech. "Kill me, sword," he said, putting the sword under his arm. "Die! Die! Die! I am dying! Now I am dead!"

Thisbe found his body. "Are you sleeping, my love? Oh no! You're dead!" She took his sword and killed herself. "Goodbye! Now I am dead, too."

Asleep, my love?
What, dead, my dove?

"This is the silliest thing I've ever seen," laughed Hippolyta.

"Shall we explain the play some more?" asked Bottom. "Or shall we do a dance?"

"No more explaining, please," said Theseus. "Let's see your dance, and then we'll say goodnight."

So, good night unto you all.

The guests and the actors had left, and the hall was dark. A few tiny lights appeared as Oberon, Titania and the fairies came in.

"Go through the house with light and music," said Oberon. "Bring happiness to all these young people. Let them have long lives together, loving each other and living in peace with their families."

"Sing and dance, and work your magic," said Titania. "Meet me all before the morning light." Fairy music sounded, and they danced out of the room.

Somewhere in Athens, a workman smiled in his sleep. He was dreaming of a beautiful lady, and of a crown of summer flowers between his long, hairy ears.

About Shakespeare

William Shakespeare lived in London over 400 years ago. Around that time, many new "playhouses" had recently opened, and they were very popular. Even Queen Elizabeth I went to see Shakespeare's plays. For ordinary people, the plays weren't expensive if you watched them standing up.

In Shakespeare's time, there were no women actors. Hermia, Helena, Hippolyta and Titania's parts were all written for boys. Shakespeare was an actor too. Perhaps he acted in *A Midsummer Night's Dream* when it was first performed.

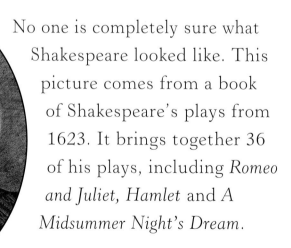

No one is completely sure what Shakespeare looked like. This picture comes from a book of Shakespeare's plays from 1623. It brings together 36 of his plays, including *Romeo and Juliet*, *Hamlet* and *A Midsummer Night's Dream*.

Activities

The answers are on page 48.

Which two people?

Finish each sentence with the names
of two people from the story.

Hippolyta   Theseus   Egeus   Demetrius   Hermia   Lysander

1. .... and .... are getting married in four days.

2. .... has come to ask .... for help.

3. .... and .... want to marry Hermia.

4. .... says .... should obey her father.

5. .... and .... plan to run away together.

What happened when?

Can you put the pictures and sentences in order?

A.

Theseus found the four young people lying on the ground.

B.

"I love Helena more than you do," said Demetrius.

C.

Puck dripped juice into Lysander's eyes.

D.

"Tomorrow, all will be well," said Puck.

E.

"Now you're both laughing at me," said Helena.

F.

"Let's have three weddings," said Theseus.

G.

"Puck, this is all your fault," said Oberon.

H.

"You're the one I love," said Lysander to Helena.

I.

"Lysander and I are running away," said Hermia.

What do they want?

Match up the speech bubbles with the characters.

Duke Theseus

Egeus

Hermia

Helena

Oberon

Titania

A. I want to marry Lysander.

B. I want my daughter to marry Demetrius.

C. I want to take care of my friend's son.

D. I want everyone in Athens to celebrate my wedding.

E. I want Titania's boy to be my servant.

F. I want Demetrius to love me again.

How did they say it?

Choose a word from the list to finish each sentence.

1.

"I play tricks on people,"
said Puck ....

2.

The Fairy King and Queen
stared at each other ....

3.

"EE-AW, EE-AW," Bottom
sang ....

4.

Titania looked ....
at Bottom.

5.

Hermia turned ....
to Helena.

angrily nervously
adoringly truly
proudly gently
loudly desperately
coldly quickly

Puck's tricks

These pictures show Puck's tricks.
Choose a sentence for each picture.

1.

A. Puck made Titania
fall in love with a donkey.

B. Puck made Titania
fall over a donkey.

2.

A. Puck told a joke in the
two men's voices.

B. Puck spoke in the
two men's voices.

3.

A. Puck gave Bottom
long, hairy ears.

B. Puck gave Bottom
strong, fairy ears.

4.

A. Puck made Lysander and
Demetrius laugh at Helena.

B. Puck made Lysander and
Demetrius fall in love with Helena.

Word list

actor (n) a person who has a part in a play.

adore (v) when you adore someone, you love them very much.

Athenian (adj) a person who comes from the city of Athens.

beg (v) to ask for something in a desperate way.

celebrate (v) when you are really happy about something, you celebrate, for example by having a party.

chase (v) to run after someone or something and try to catch them.

cheerful (adj) generally happy.

clearing (n) an open space between the trees in a wood or a forest.

comedy (n) a play that is funny or generally happy.

convent (n) a place where nuns live. Nuns are women who have promised to live their lives for God, and who will never marry.

darling (n) a word for someone you love very much.

donkey (n) an animal like a horse, but smaller, with long ears.

Duke (n) an important lord, almost as important as a king.

hay (n) dried grass. Horses and other animals eat hay.

lantern (n) something people used to carry to give light. Lanterns were usually made of metal and glass, with a candle inside.

lips (n) the edges of your mouth.

make fun of someone (v) if you make fun of someone, you laugh at them in an unkind way.

obey (v) when you obey someone, you do whatever they tell you.

perform (v) when you perform, you act or
sing or play music or dance for other people.

pretend (v) when you pretend, you make someone
believe something that isn't true or isn't real.

punish (v) if you punish someone, you make
them pay in some way for doing something wrong.

roar (v) when a wild animal roars, it makes
a loud noise to frighten other animals.

run away (v) to escape from a person or a place.

save (v) when you save someone, you protect
them and keep them out of danger.

scratch (v) to hurt someone or damage something using
your fingernails, or an animal might use its claws.

speech (n) when an actor speaks on his own about a subject.

stroke (v) when you stroke an animal, you move your
hand gently over its fur to make it comfortable.

temper (n) your mood, and especially how
often or how easily you become angry.

thee (pron) an old-fashioned way of saying "you".

tragic (adj) if a story or a play is tragic, it is very sad,
and often ends with one or more of the characters dying.

unto (prep) an old-fashioned way of saying "to".

wander (v) when you wander, you walk slowly
and you are not sure where you are going.

Answers

Which two people?
1. Hippolyta, Theseus
2. Egeus, Theseus
3. Demetrius, Lysander
4. Theseus, Hermia
5. Hermia, Lysander

What happened when?
I, C, H, E, B,
G, D, A, F

What do they want?
Duke Theseus: D
Egeus: B
Hermia: A
Helena: F
Oberon: E
Titania: C

How did they say it?
1. proudly
2. coldly
3. loudly
4. adoringly
5. angrily

Puck's tricks
1. A
2. B
3. A
4. B

You can find information about other
Usborne English Readers here:
www.usborneenglishreaders.com

Designed by Caroline Day & Jodie Smith
Series designer: Laura Nelson
Edited by Jane Chisholm
With thanks to Rosie Hore
Digital imaging: Nick Wakeford

Page 40: engraving of William Shakespeare © Universal History Archive/UIG via Getty Images

First published in 2017 by Usborne Publishing Ltd.,
Usborne House, 83-85 Saffron Hill, London EC1N 8RT, England.
www.usborne.com Copyright © 2017 Usborne Publishing Ltd.